LOGICAL LOGIC

A Super Collection of Activities to Develop Critical Thinking and Problem-Solving Skills

Grades 5–8

FACTS & OPINIONS

BARRIERS TO

INFERENCES

DEDUCTIVE REASONING

DENOTATION

RELEVANCE

SYLLOGISMS

ANALOGIES

LOGICAL THINKING

CONNOTATION

Written by Barbara Gregorich • Illustrated by Beverly Armstrong
Cover Design by Kathy Parks

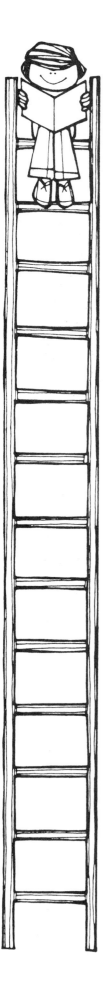

The Learning Works

Edited by Sherri M. Butterfield

The purchase of this book entitles the individual teacher to reproduce copies for use in the classroom.

The reproduction of any part for an entire school or school system or for commercial use is strictly prohibited.

No form of this work may be reproduced or transmitted or recorded without written permission from the publisher.

Introduction

Logical Logic is a special collection of reproducible activities designed to develop critical thinking skills and to improve oral and written communication. These activities are grouped in eight sections: (1) Facts and Opinions, (2) Denotation and Connotation, (3) Relevance, (4) Barriers to Logical Thinking, (5) Analogies, (6) Inferences, (7) Deductive Reasoning, and (8) Syllogisms. They will help your students distinguish facts from opinions, understand denotation and connotation, recognize double standards and glittering generalities, create analogies, make inferences, select relevant responses, understand deductive reasoning, and evaluate premises and syllogisms.

The activities in this book have been arranged in logical sequence so that each one builds on the concepts and skills taught before and leads to the concepts and skills that are introduced later. For this reason, you are encouraged to use these activities in the order in which they are presented. So that you can see how the skills are interrelated and select the activities your students need, each activity sheet has been identified by both skill and title in the table of contents.

Because many of the skills associated with logical thinking cannot be mastered without considerable practice, you may find it useful to augment the activities in this book in some of the following ways:

Opinions Only—Obtain facts from an almanac or book of records. Have students rewrite each fact as a statement that expresses a related attitude, evaluation, or judgment.

Dialogue Delight—Have students write dialogues in which they incorporate a variety of irrelevant responses to statements and questions. Stage some of these dialogues as plays and see if other students can identify the flaws and correct them.

Infer Away—Discuss the picture on page 35 and possible reasons for differences in the inferences students have made about it. Then find other pictures of scenes or events that are open to interpretation, post them in the classroom, and encourage students to infer away.

What Can You Deduce?—Have students create problems in deductive reasoning for other students to solve using matrices.

Statements and Terms—Provide trios of related terms and challenge students to use them in syllogisms. Evaluate these syllogisms to determine if they are valid or invalid and if the premises on which they are based are true or false.

Contents

Contents
(continued)

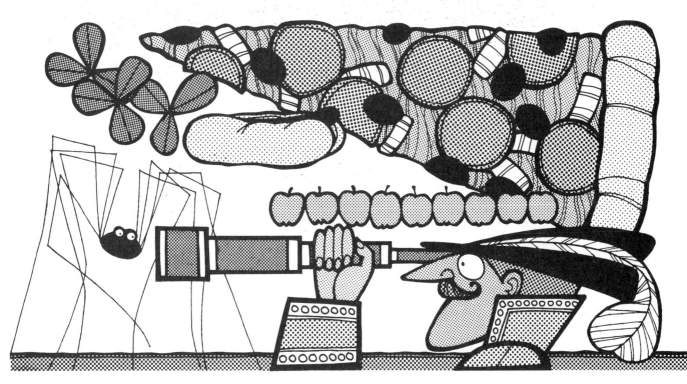

Is That a Fact?

The English word **fact** comes from the Latin word *factum,* which means "that which is done; a deed, act, exploit, or achievement." A fact is a deed, an act, or something that has been done. It is also a statement about something that really exists or has actually happened. A fact is a statement that has been or can be proved to be true.

The word fact has no antonym, which means that there is no one word that is *exactly* opposite to it in meaning. There are, however, several words that name contrasting concepts: (1) **Fiction** is not fact. Fiction is the product of imagination. While it is a fact that Nobel laureate William Golding wrote a novel entitled *Lord of the Flies,* the characters and events in this book were imagined and created by Golding. The book is fiction, not fact. (2) **Opinion** is also not fact. An opinion is a statement based on feelings or beliefs which expresses an attitude, conclusion, evaluation, or judgment. An opinion may be about something that has actually happened, but it cannot be proved. For example, it is an opinion that *Lord of the Flies* is a great book. It is also an opinion that it is a bad book, an important book, a misunderstood book, or a strange book. (3) An **order** is not a fact. An order is a statement requiring or commanding that something be done. The sentence "You must read *Lord of the Flies* by next Monday" is an order, but it is not a fact. (4) A **judgment** is also not a fact. A judgment is a statement of opinion about something that has happened or something that has been done.

Read each statement below. Circle the numbers of the statements that are facts.

1. Columbus landed on a Caribbean island in 1492.

2. Columbus Day should be celebrated on October 12, not on the second Monday in October.

3. Magma is hot liquid rock inside the earth.

4. The explosion of Mount St. Helens was the worst U.S. disaster of the decade.

5. The Arctic is the last frontier on earth.

6. Points on the Arctic Circle lie approximately 66½ degrees north of the equator.

7. A typewriter is a machine that produces letters on paper mechanically.

8. Janine's favorite gift was the opera glasses her great-grandmother gave her.

9. *Sedum morganianum* is the Latin name for a plant popularly known as donkey tail or burro tail.

10. Never mess with a Taurus.

Name_____

Seeking Verification

Facts are statements that can be checked. They can be proved true, or **verified**, by demonstration, evidence, or testimony. Sometimes, when you attempt to verify a statement, you discover that it is *not* a fact because the information it contains is incorrect or untrue.

Read the statements below. Check each one in the source listed. If you can verify the statement, write **V** on the line in front of the number. If you cannot verify the statement, write **N** on the line. Then, in the comment box, explain what is wrong with the statement and why it is **not** a fact.

Statement	Source	Comment
_____ **1.** An oxeye is a type of flowering plant.	dictionary	
_____ **2.** Louisiana's northern border is the thirty-second parallel.	atlas	
_____ **3.** Nathan Hale said, "I know not what course others may take, but as for me, give me liberty or give me death!"	*Bartlett's Familiar Quotations*	
_____ **4.** Babe Didrikson's first name was Mildred.	encyclopedia	
_____ **5.** Ty Cobb won the American League batting championship for twelve years.	almanac	

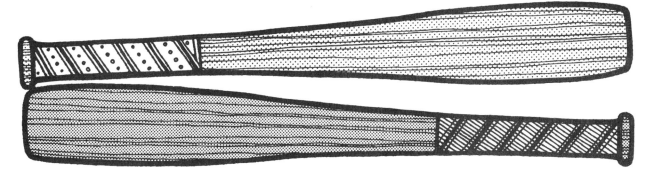

Name_____

Now It Is, Now It Isn't

Opinions are not facts. Opinions are statements based on feelings or beliefs. They express attitudes, conclusions, evaluations, or judgments. Opinions often contain such words as *best* or *worst, beautiful* or *ugly, right* or *wrong.*

Change each of the facts below into an opinion by rewriting it to express an attitude, evaluation, or judgment. An example has been done for you.

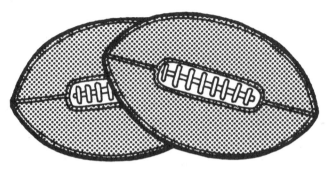

Example

Fact: In 1982, members of the National Football League went on strike.

Opinion: *When NFL football players went on strike in 1982, they showed nothing but contempt for their millions of fans.*

1. Fact: Archie Griffin, a running back from Ohio State, is the only college football player to win the Heisman Trophy two years in a row.

Opinion: _____

_____

2. Fact: George Halas, Vince Lombardi, and Norm Van Brocklin have all been inducted into the Pro Football Hall of Fame in Canton, Ohio.

Opinion: _____

_____

3. Fact: According to Nielsen viewer composition analyses, the television viewing audience for the NFL Superbowl is 62 percent men and 38 percent women.

Opinion: _____

_____

4. Fact: According to the Nielsen ratings, nearly twice as many people watch the football Superbowl as watch the baseball World Series.

Opinion: _____

_____

5. Fact: George Blanda holds the career record for having had the most passes intercepted, but he is also football's leading lifetime scorer.

Opinion: _____

Name_____

Opinions! Opinions!

There are four basic types of opinions: (1) **Generalizations** are statements about entire groups of things. (2) **Judgments** are evaluations of a person, action, or thing. They declare it to be *good* or *bad, beautiful* or *ugly, right* or *wrong, delightful* or *boring, valuable* or *worthless*. (3) **Orders** emphasize that an action *must* be taken, that something *should* be done. (4) **Predictions** assert that something will happen, often if certain conditions are or are not met.

An opinion can be of more than one type. For example, the statement "That duck is noisy" is a judgment, while the statement "All ducks are noisy" is both a generalization and a judgment.

The statements below express opinions. Label each statement to indicate what type of opinion statement it is. Write **G** on the line for each statement that is a **generalization**, **J** for each statement that is a **judgment**, **O** for each statement that is an **order**, and **P** for each statement that is a **prediction.** Because some statements are of more than one type, you will need to write more than one letter on some of the lines.

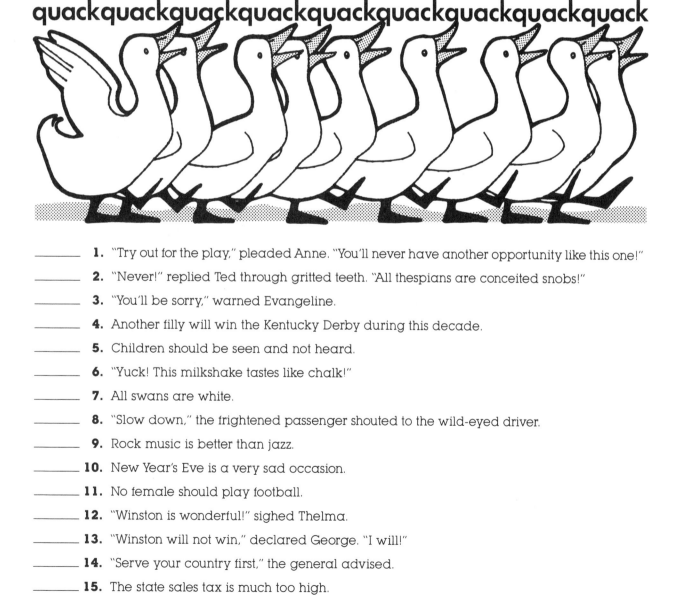

_____ **1.** "Try out for the play," pleaded Anne. "You'll never have another opportunity like this one!"

_____ **2.** "Never!" replied Ted through gritted teeth. "All thespians are conceited snobs!"

_____ **3.** "You'll be sorry," warned Evangeline.

_____ **4.** Another filly will win the Kentucky Derby during this decade.

_____ **5.** Children should be seen and not heard.

_____ **6.** "Yuck! This milkshake tastes like chalk!"

_____ **7.** All swans are white.

_____ **8.** "Slow down," the frightened passenger shouted to the wild-eyed driver.

_____ **9.** Rock music is better than jazz.

_____ **10.** New Year's Eve is a very sad occasion.

_____ **11.** No female should play football.

_____ **12.** "Winston is wonderful!" sighed Thelma.

_____ **13.** "Winston will not win," declared George. "I will!"

_____ **14.** "Serve your country first," the general advised.

_____ **15.** The state sales tax is much too high.

Name_____

Get the Facts, Please

Below is an article about American automobile manufacturing. The article contains the writer's opinions, but no facts. You can make the writer's argument a stronger, more convincing one by supplying the facts. Look them up under *automobile production* in an almanac.

In the late 1970s, American automobile manufacturers found themselves in serious trouble. All but one of the major automakers produced fewer cars during this period than they had in the 1960s. In 1965, for example, American Motors Corporation produced _____ cars. In 1978, however, it manufactured only _____. Its production had been cut in half, and it was barely solvent.

But American Motors is not one of the so-called big three automakers, so let's take a look at Ford. In 1965, the Ford Motor Company produced _____ cars. Six years later, in 1979, it produced only _____ automobiles. While this drop in production was not as severe as that experienced by American Motors, it was still a downward trend.

In 1965, Chrysler Corporation manufactured a total of _____ automobiles. By 1975, this number had dropped to _____. In 1978, it climbed to _____; but in 1979, it was back down to _____ cars, and Chrysler was in serious financial trouble.

Only General Motors, the giant among giants, produced more cars in 1979 than it had in 1965. In 1965, GM produced _____ cars. In 1979, it manufactured _____ cars. But even GM had some bad years. In 1970 and in 1975, it produced only _____ and _____ automobiles, respectively.

What does this downward trend in auto manufacturing reflect? Perhaps it shows that, during the 1970s, Americans did not have the money to change cars as often as they did in the 1960s. Perhaps it shows that American automobile designers fell behind the times and failed to create cars that were both comfortable and economical. Perhaps it shows that Americans were buying more foreign cars. Perhaps the downward trend reflects a combination of these factors. Whatever the reason, however, it is clear that American automobile manfacturers experienced a severe slump in the 1970s and were forced to compete more aggressively for the U.S. transportation dollar.

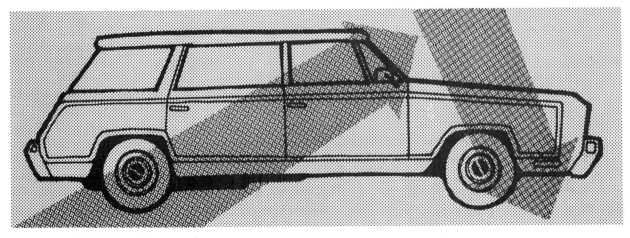

Name_____

Watch Those Numbers!

According to an old saying, figures don't lie, but liars do figure. The point is that people often use numerical data, called **statistics,** to make their arguments more persuasive. Sometimes, these statistics take the form of **percentages,** parts of a whole expressed in hundredths.

The use of percentages in an argument can be misleading. Large percentages may appear disproportionately alarming. Small percentages may appear inaccurately insignificant.

The real impact, or importance, of a percentage depends on the larger number on which it is based or of which it expresses a part. For example, the percentage in the statement "Crime has risen in our town by *50 percent* this year" sounds frighteningly large unless one is also told that only two crimes were committed in the town last year. Then, the 50 percent increase represents only one additional crime, for an annual total of three—a figure that is not so frightening after all. On the other hand, a 2 percent increase might seem relatively small—unless one is also told that the number on which this percentage is based is two billion!

Assume that you are disputing the opinions given below. First, read each opinion. Second, read the fact that accompanies it. Third, calculate the actual number represented by the percentage. Finally, use this knowledge to write a sentence refuting the opinion.

1. **Opinion:** *There's no need for alarm. This year's budget is up only 8 percent.*
   Fact: Last year's budget was $94,000,000.
   Sentence: _____
   _____

2. **Opinion:** *We need to raise health standards in this country. The number of reported measles cases has increased 100 percent.*
   Fact: Last year there were two cases of measles.
   Sentence: _____
   _____

3. **Opinion:** *With all due respect, I am proposing a mere 6 percent increase in defense spending.*
   Fact: Last year $10,600,600,000 was spent on defense.
   Sentence: _____
   _____

4. **Opinion:** *Everyone's leaving town! There are 11 percent fewer people this year than there were last year.*
   Fact: Last year the population of the town was three hundred people.
   Sentence: _____
   _____

5. **Opinion:** *The rat population is up only 2½ percent this year.*
   Fact: Last year there were 9,700,000 rats.
   Sentence: _____

Says Who?

Some people attempt to substantiate their arguments with the opinions of recognized authorities. If the authorities they select are knowledgeable about the subject being discussed and have expressed relevant opinions, quoting these opinions may, indeed, strengthen an argument. But watch out for the "authority" who is inadequately identified, who is from the past, or whose expertise is in an entirely different area.

For example, **vague authorities** are cited in the following statement: "*Lawyers* say that criminals should be punished severely." Here, the supposed opinion of an authority group—lawyers—is being used to give increased weight to an argument; but it is unlikely that all lawyers share this opinion. To be persuasive, the statement should say which lawyers, where, and under what circumstances.

A **past authority** is cited in this statement: "*Cicero* says that only the rich should govern." Cicero may not have said it. If he did say it, his doing so does not make it true; and even if it was true or appropriate for the time in which Cicero lived, it may not be true or applicable now.

An **irrelevant authority** is cited in this statement: "Our *football coach* says that free trade is a dumb idea." Here, the opinion of an authority figure in one area (sports) is being used to support an argument in another area (economics). What the authority figure says may be interesting, but it does not increase our real knowledge of the problem (trade) being discussed.

The opinion expressed in each of the sentences below is attributed to some authority. Read these sentences carefully. Circle the name of the authority being cited in each one. Then label each of these authorities by writing one letter on the line in front of each sentence. Write **V** for a **vague authority, P** for a **past authority,** and **I** for an **irrelevant authority.** Because some authorities fit more than one of these labels, you will need to decide which label is most appropriate.

_____ **1.** Automakers have said that air bags may open unexpectedly and cause accidents.

_____ **2.** My uncle, the fire chief, says that Franklin Roosevelt was the finest president this country has ever had.

_____ **3.** According to the Greek playwright Sophocles, the devil is wise.

_____ **4.** Many writers assert that Webster's dictionary is the best.

_____ **5.** Dogs prefer moist food to dry food by a three-to-one margin.

_____ **6.** According to my landlord, Ford cars are much better designed than GM cars.

_____ **7.** Musicians all agree that Johann Sebastian Bach was a greater composer than George Frederick Handel.

_____ **8.** My great-aunt, who is a spinster, believes that children should be seen and not heard.

_____ **9.** Speaker of the House Sam Rayburn (1882–1961) said that the greatest domestic problem facing the United States was saving our soil and water.

_____ **10.** History has proved that Rayburn was right.

_____ **11.** British playwright George Bernard Shaw (1856–1950) observed that Americans have no sense of privacy.

_____ **12.** According to American editor and satirist H. L. Mencken (1880–1956), no one ever went broke underestimating the taste of the American people.

_____ **13.** Representatives of the major oil companies assert that current product prices do not provide enough profit margin with which these companies can carry out needed exploration and develop reserves.

_____ **14.** Horse trainers agree that Arabian horses are easier to handle than Thoroughbreds.

_____ **15.** Sports announcers say that basketball players must work harder and be better conditioned than football players.

Name_____

Might and Right

Another method of strengthening an argument is with the threat of physical force. This method is called **argumentum ad baculum,** a Latin phrase which means, literally, "argument by the stick, or shepherd's staff," in other words, "proof by force."

Does might make right? Is the threat of force or punishment a good reason for accepting a belief? Or should a person be willing to suffer punishment, even imprisonment, for the freedom of believing as he chooses?

In 1842, American teacher, philosopher, and writer Henry David Thoreau (1817–1862) refused to pay a tax because he did not want his money used to support a government that was waging war against Mexico and that permitted slavery.

Thoreau wrote an essay entitled "On the Duty of Civil Disobedience" in which he explained his actions. Below are excerpts from this essay. Read them carefully. On the lines at the bottom of this page, summarize what Thoreau is saying, tell whether you agree or disagree with his conclusions, and explain why you feel as you do.

After all, the practical reason why, when the power is once in the hands of the people, a majority are permitted, and for a long period continue, to rule, is not because they are most likely to be in the right, nor because this seems fairest to the minority, but because they are physically the strongest. But a government in which the majority rule in all cases cannot be based on justice, even as far as men understand it.... Must the citizen ever for a moment, or in the least degree, resign his conscience to the legislator? Why has every man a conscience, then? ... It is not desirable to cultivate a respect for the law, so much as for the right. The only obligation which I have a right to assume is to do at any time what I think right.

_____

_____

_____

_____

_____

_____

_____

_____

_____

_____

Meaning What?

To evaluate an opinion, one must clearly understand the meanings of the words used to express that opinion. Most words have two levels of meaning, the denotative and the connotative. A word's denotative meaning, or **denotation,** is its dictionary definition, or its literal meaning. For example, the word *dog* denotes "an animal of the species *Canis familiaris."*

Like many other words, *dog* also has a second level of meaning, a **connotation.** This level includes the associations and suggestions that the word arouses in the user, the reader, or the listener. For example, to many people, the word *dog* suggests not only an animal of a particular species but also the qualities of warmth, companionship,

and loyalty, which are often associated with that animal; however, for people who have been bitten by a *dog*, this word may arouse unpleasant memories and cause them to respond with feelings of fear or apprehension. Thus, while the denotation of a word remains relatively constant, its connotation may change from time to time and vary from person to person.

As a further illustration of the powerful effect of connotations, note that the words *dog* and *cur* are synonyms, that is, their denotations are the same; but their connotations are quite different. *Cur* connotes a certain *type* of dog, "a mongrel or inferior dog," and is also used to mean "a surly or cowardly person."

Match the words listed below with their denotations, or dictionary definitions, by writing the correct letter on each line.

_____	**1.** bagel	**a.**	member of a police force (slang)
_____	**2.** clover	**b.**	low, leguminous herb with three leaflets and dense clusters of small flowers
_____	**3.** cop	**c.**	having a compact, heavy build
_____	**4.** desegregate	**d.**	belonging to a place by birth; grown, produced, or originating in a certain place
_____	**5.** façade	**e.**	to join together by twisting
_____	**6.** frilly	**f.**	inhabitant of Russia
_____	**7.** garbage	**g.**	ruffled, gathered, or pleated
_____	**8.** grapple	**h.**	musical instrument that has many strings of graded length stretched across an open, triangular frame with a curving top and that is played by plucking with the fingers
_____	**9.** harp	**i.**	ring-shaped, chewy bread
_____	**10.** heavyset	**j.**	food wastes; trash
_____	**11.** intertwine	**k.**	wooden club or cudgel (named for a town in Ireland that is famous for its oak trees)
_____	**12.** native	**l.**	the face or front of a building
_____	**13.** Russian	**m.**	to hold onto something, as with an iron hook
_____	**14.** sentry	**n.**	to abolish arbitary separation based on inappropriate, unfair, or superficial distinctions
_____	**15.** shillelagh	**o.**	guard

Name_____

How Do You Respond?

The **denotation** of a word is its dictionary definition, its literal meaning. The **connotation** of a word is the shading given its literal meaning by experience or association. For example, the words *inexpensive* and *cheap* are synonyms because they have the same denotation, or literal meaning, "reasonable in price"; but *cheap* also means "of inferior quality or worth" and connotes something that is sleazy or tawdry.

How do you respond to the words listed below? What connotation does each one have for you? Circle the term in parentheses that best describes your response to the word and explain your choice on the lines. Your answers may differ from those of your classmates.

1. **artist** (conventional/unconventional): _____

_____

2. **clover** (lucky/neutral/unlucky): _____

_____

3. **cop** (helpful/unhelpful/obstructive): _____

_____

4. **façade** (genuine/artificial): _____

_____

5. **frilly** (serious/merely decorative/frivolous): _____

_____

6. **harp** (soothing/enjoyable/irritating): _____

_____

7. **politician** (honest/dishonest): _____

_____

8. **Russian** (peace-loving/neutral/bellicose): _____

_____

9. **bug** (interesting/disgusting/alarming): _____

_____

10. **insect** (fascinating/frightening): _____

_____

Name_____

What Do You Say?

Two words can have similar denotations, as do words like *dog* and *cur* or *inexpensive* and *cheap*, yet have very different connotations. The impact of a sentence is determined by both the denotations and the connotations of the words used in it. For example, consider the difference between saying, "After a long and rewarding life, Martin Magillicuddy *passed away* quietly at his home," and saying, "After a long and rewarding life, Martin Magillicuddy *bit the dust*." both of these phrases—*passed away* and *bit the dust*—

mean "died," yet each has a far different impact on the reader or hearer. *Passed away* connotes a gentle transition from life to what lies beyond. *Bit the dust* is disrespectful and would be appropriate only in a western or humorous context. *Died* is abrupt, humorless, and painfully matter-of-fact.

Read the sentences below. For each one, explain the connotations of the two words or phrases in parentheses. Then, select and circle one of them to complete the sentence and give it the shade of meaning you feel is appropriate.

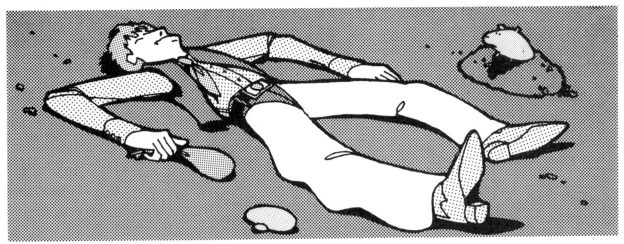

1. Athletes (**sweat/perspire**) when they exercise.

   sweat: _____

   perspire: _____

2. If you are here to apply for a job, please ask the (**girl/woman**) at the front desk for an application.

   girl: _____

   woman: _____

3. "There's a (**bug/insect**) in my soup!" screamed the customer.

   bug: _____

   insect: _____

4. The door was answered by a tall, dark, and handsome (**male/man**).

   male: _____

   man: _____

5. The (**teenager's/young person's**) behavior annoyed me.

   teenager's: _____

   young person's: _____

Name_____

In a Pickle

In each statement below, there is one term whose meaning, or denotation, is incorrect. Circle this term and explain the error. Use an almanac, dictionary, or encyclopedia to check facts and meanings.

1. British refusal to allow the United States to be represented in Parliament was an important cause of the American Revolution.

_____
_____
_____

2. We must realize that the United States possesses limited supplies of such vital natural resources as coal, oil, and steel.

_____
_____
_____

3. Mark grew an abundance of green beans, pickles, sweet corn, and tomatoes in his garden.

_____
_____
_____

4. "Tides are the occasional risings and fallings of large bodies of water. They are caused in part by the gravitational attraction of the moon, and there are two tides in each twenty-four-hour period," said the professor. "In each lunar day of twenty-four hours, there are two tides," wrote the note-taking student.

_____
_____
_____

5. "If your dog is bothered by tics, a flea collar might help," advised the newsletter.

_____
_____
_____

6. The car in front of Susan spun out of control on the icy, snow-covered street. Carefully, Susan applied the brakes; but her car, too, went into a spin. She closed her eyes and felt the cars collide with a sickening thud. Hesitantly, Susan opened her eyes. She sighed with relief as she realized that she was unhurt. Then, she thought of the other driver. Quickly, she got out of her car and ran to the other vehicle. She could tell at a glance that the driver was dead. She had murdered him.

_____
_____
_____

Round and Round

Circular definitions are ones in which each element depends for its meaning or understanding on another element which depends, in turn, on the first element. Because of the interdependence of the elements, you cannot understand without already knowing. For example, consider the following conversation between a puzzled student and a less-than-helpful teacher:

Student: Teacher, what is the meaning of the word *canine*?

Teacher: *Canine* is an adjective meaning "of the family Canidae."

Student: But what does *Canidae* mean?

Teacher: That's easy! *Canidae* is the *canine* family.

In his search for knowledge, the poor student has come full circle, back to *canine*, and knows no more than he did when he started. How much more helpful it would have been if the teacher had responded to the first question by explaining that *canine* is an adjective meaning "of or relating to dogs or to the family Canidae, which includes dogs, wolves, jackals, and foxes." By mentioning the familiar word *dogs* and giving specific examples of members of the Canidae family, the teacher could have helped the student understand both words, *canine* and *Canidae*."

The cartoon strip below illustrates the problems associated with circular definitions or explanations. For this strip, explain what is being defined in a circular way and rewrite the conversation in the last frame to eliminate the circularity.

1. What is being defined or described? _____

2. Your rewritten version: _____

_____

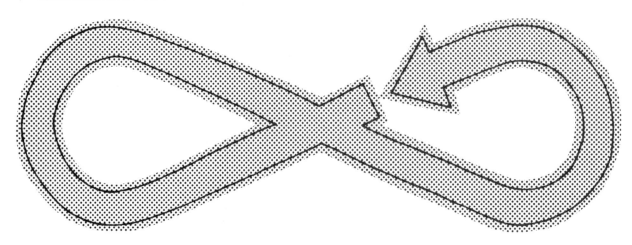

Name_____

How Does That Fit?

Relevance is "relation to the matter at hand; practical applicability." Thus, a statement that is **relevant** to a discussion is one that offers evidence tending to prove or disprove the matter being discussed. **Irrelevant** statements may provide interesting or useful information, but they do nothing to further the discussion. As an example, consider the following brief conversation:

Coach: Smith, why did you drop that pass?
Smith: I was wearing a new number on my jersey, Coach.

Smith's response may be a true statement, and it may offer interesting or useful information; but it does not appear to answer the coach's question. If Smith had gone on to explain that the new number had made it more difficult for the quarterback to identify him and had, therefore, unnecessarily delayed the pass, which was then hastily and inaccurately thrown, the new number might, indeed, have been relevant. As it is, there is no apparent connection between it and the dropped pass.

Poor Alice is having one of those days. Everywhere she goes, someone wants to know why she has or has not done something. Help Alice respond to these questions. Read the numbered questions and the lettered responses carefully. Then, on the line beside each question, write the letter or letters of any responses that would be relevant.

_____ **1. Teacher:**   Alice, you're late for your fifth-period class.

_____ **2. Coach:**   Alice, that's your slowest time all year in the 500-meter race.

_____ **3. Mother:**   Alice, why didn't you clean your room this morning?

_____ **4. Sister:**   Alice, why are you wearing *my* new, navy sweater?

_____ **5. Brother:**   Alice, this cake tastes burned.

a. I woke up late and barely had time to eat and dress.
b. I was wearing my blue gym shorts.
c. It was ninety degrees in the shade out there!
d. Mr. Smith, my sixth period teacher, kept me after class.
e. I only mixed the batter. Mom did the rest.
f. The bells weren't working this afternoon.
g. I've felt sick since I hurried through breakfast this morning.
h. I didn't have any clean clothes.
i. I am going to a rock concert tonight.
j. I saw a good movie last night.
k. Dad got so interested in the article he was reading that he forgot to turn off the oven.
l. Babe Didrickson was my favorite female track star.
m. Mom, Dad, and I think it's just right.
n. I stumbled during the last lap.
o. Well, it's the only thing that matches *my* plaid skirt.

Speak to Me, Please!

Assume that you are going to argue against the numbered statements below. Read each one, select the lettered response—either **a** or **b**—that would be most relevant, and circle the letter. Then, on each line lettered **c**, write another sentence that is relevant to both the numbered statement and your selected response.

1. The Dallas Cowboys are the best team in professional football.

    a. My favorite team is the Los Angeles Rams.

    b. The Cowboy defensive line is weak this year.

    c. _____

2. You need a haircut!

    a. I've decided to change my hairstyle.

    b. I look funny in short hair.

    c. _____

3. You'll *never* learn to play chess!

    a. I've been reading a book about chess, which I borrowed from the library.

    b. Neither will you!

    c. _____

4. The earth is flat.

    a. According to scientific evidence, the earth is a spheroid.

    b. A large percentage of the earth's surface is covered by water.

    c. _____

5. To stay healthy, one should exercise hard every day.

    a. Some Americans jog while others swim or play tennis.

    b. Too much exercise can be as unhealthful as too little.

    c. _____

Does It Follow?

One stumbling block to effective communication, whether it be written or oral, is the *non sequitur*. **Non sequitur** is a Latin phrase that means "it does not follow." A *non sequitur* is a statement or response that does not follow logically from anything that has been said previously. In formal logic, it is an inference that does not follow from the premises.

In the following dialogue, James's reply is a *non sequitur*.

Teacher: James, do you know who released all of the frogs in the biology lab?
James: I saw one hopping down the hall.

Deliberately or unknowingly, James has failed to respond logically to the teacher's question. The only logical response he could have given was either "yes" or "no."

For each numbered item below, identify the question, problem, or premise and the *non sequitur*. Then, write one logical solution or response.

1. **Customer:** I bought this record yesterday. When I played it for the first time last night, I discovered that it is warped. I want to exchange it.

   Salesperson: That's a terrible record! Their first album was much better.

   a. Problem: _____

   b. *Non sequitur:* _____

   c. Logical response: _____

   _____

2. **Employee:** When I was talking with the other office secretary, Tom Braden, I discovered that his salary is much higher than mine. Shouldn't women receive equal pay for equal work?
   Employer: Women miss a lot of workdays.

   a. Question: _____

   b. *Non sequitur:* _____

   c. Logical response: _____

   _____

3. **Doctor:** As your doctor, I strongly urge you to stop smoking immediately.
   Patient: Do you smoke, Doctor?
   Doctor: I think I'm qualified to take care of my own health, don't you?

   a. Question: _____

   b. *Non sequitur:* _____

   c. Logical response: _____

   _____

4. **Announcer:** In Hollywood, where beauty is money, glamorous stars rely on Lovelier-You Lotion to care for their delicate complexions. If the stars trust it, shouldn't you try it?

   a. Premise: _____

   b. *Non sequitur:* _____

   c. Logical response: _____

   _____

Address the Issue

Another stumbling block to effective communication, especially oral communication, is *argumentum ad hominem*. **Argumentum ad hominem** is a Latin phrase that literally means "argument to the man." An *argumentum ad hominem* is an argument or reply that appeals to the hearer's emotions rather than to his intellect or one that is marked by an attack on an opponent's character rather than an answer to his contentions. Thus, an *ad hominem* reply is closely related to *non sequitur* in that it is, likewise, not a logical response to what has gone before, is not directly relevant to the topic being discussed, and does not, in any way, help to resolve the issue.

The campaign speeches that precede local, state, and national elections are replete with examples of *argumentum ad hominem*. Notice how this device is used in the following excerpt from a fictional exchange between the incumbent, Senator Unaware, and the challenger, Roger Runamuck.

Runamuck: The senator's record on the issues is appalling. He always favors big business and increased military spending.

Unaware: Friends, my worthy opponent here hasn't publicized his military service record, and I wonder why, don't you?

Runamuck: Now Senator, you know perfectly well that there is nothing wrong with my service record.

Unaware: Nothing wrong? But let's not dwell on that issue. We have a lot of ground to cover tonight.

Runamuck: Not so fast, Senator. I want to clear up this matter before we go on.

Unaware: And I don't blame you, son. You surely don't want to leave any doubt or confusion in the minds of my constituents.

Runamuck: You know perfectly well that I am as patriotic as you are, even though my asthma kept me from enlisting.

Unaware: My worthy opponent, Mr. Runamuck, seems to be long on excuses but a bit short on record. Now you remember that, my friends, when you go to the polls.

In this passage, the more experienced politician, Senator Unaware, has skillfully used *argumentum ad hominem* to avoid having to respond to Runamuck's accusations that he has repeatedly voted in favor of big business and increased military spending. By appealing to the audience's emotions and suggesting that there is something wrong with Runamuck's military service record and, therefore, his character, Senator Unaware has put Runamuck very much on the defensive.

Pretend that strict rules have now been imposed for this exchange between senator and challenger and that *argumentum ad hominem* is not allowed. On the lines below, rewrite the dialogue as it might be if Senator Unaware made a logical and relevant reply to Runamuck's accusations. If you need additional space, continue your dialogue on a separate sheet of paper.

Runamuck: *The senator's record on the issues is appalling. He always favors big business and increased military spending.*

Unaware: _____

_____

_____

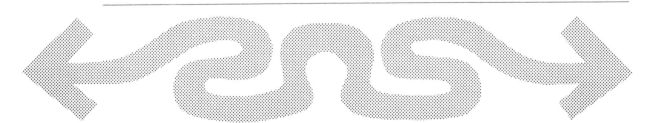

Name_____

So's Your Old Man!

Another form of irrelevance in discussion or argument is *tu quoque*. **Tu Quoque**, a Latin phrase meaning "thou also" or "you too," occurs when the accused accuses the accuser or when a person criticized for something responds by insinuating that his opponent is at least equally deserving of criticism for the same fault or shortcoming. Notice how this device is used in the following excerpt from a fictional exchange between the incumbent, Senator Unaware, and the challenger, Roger Runamuck.

Runamuck: The senator's foreign policy record is abysmal. In fact, it can be summed up in one word—aid. Obviously, he does not understand that friendship can't be bought!

Unaware: I'm glad you brought up the subject of buying friendship because it's closely related to buying votes, and that's what you're doing. You're using spending promises to buy votes!

Runamuck: What about your own promises—made at a news conference just yesterday—to keep open the defense plants in your home state?

What began as a discussion of one subject (foreign policy) has quickly degenerated into accusations related to another subject (possible vote buying) because of Senator Unaware's *argumentum ad hominem* and Runamuck's *tu quoque*.

Once again, these men obviously need help to develop a meaningful discussion. On the lines below, write a dialogue in which Unaware and Runamuck discuss some aspect of foreign policy logically, without resorting to either *argumentum ad hominem* or *tu quoque*, or write an original dialogue between two classmates in which they disagree and resort to both *argumentum ad hominem* and *tu quoque*. If you need additional space, continue your dialogue on a separate sheet of paper.

_____: _____
_____
_____
_____: _____
_____
_____
_____: _____
_____
_____
_____
_____

Name_____

Double, Double, Toil and Trouble

Another barrier to logical thinking and effective communication is failure to consistently apply similar standards in similar situations. One form this failure takes is called a **double standard.** Where a double standard prevails, a set of principles is applied differently and more rigorously to one group of people or circumstances than to another. For example, a man may insist that theft is wrong and should not go unpunished when his wallet is stolen by a pickpocket, while occasionally taking home supplies his employer has purchased for office use only. When it comes to theft, this man actually has two standards, one that he applies to his own property and another that he applies to company property.

Double standards are quite common in the thinking of some people. For each situation named below, think of a double standard you either have encountered or can imagine. State the general principle, and describe the double standard based on it.

1. Situation: A double standard that parents might apply to themselves and to their children.

   a. General principle: _____

   b. Double standard: _____

_____

2. Situation: A double standard that men might apply to themselves and to women.

   a. General principle: _____

   b. Double standard: _____

_____

3. Situation: A double standard that people of one nationality might apply to themselves and to people of a different nationality.

   a. General principle: _____

   b. Double standard: _____

_____

All That Glitters—Is Not Clear or True!

A **generality** is an imprecise, inadequate, or indefinite statement. For example, Sam Nonsmoker might assert, "Stiffer laws against smoking are needed." If you oppose smoking, you might prematurely agree; but Sam's statement is inadequate and unclear. Sam needs to define what he means by "stiffer" and to describe the legislation and penalties he has in mind. After he does so, you can evaluate his proposal and intelligently agree or disagree.

A **glittering generality** is a generality to which carefully selected words have been added because of their emotional impact. In a statement of this sort, an opinion or action one might question is associated with an abstract value one will *not* question in an attempt to avoid logical scrutiny. For example, if Sam Nonsmoker said, "Stiffer laws against smoking will make the world

a better place," he would be adding glitter but no substance to his previous generality. If you were impressed by the glitter, you might praise his avowed efforts to make the world better without questioning his methods. But if you paused to examine his statement, you might question that a single change of any sort could affect so large an area (the world), and you might ask: Better in what ways? Better for whom?

Propaganda and advertising are filled with glittering generalities. Logical questioning will usually strip away the glitter and expose these generalities for what they are. In the cartoons below, help the listeners respond to the glittering generalities by writing an appropriate question in each open conversation bubble.

And Then He Absconded

Post hoc is a shortened version of the longer Latin expression **post hoc, ergo prompter hoc,** which means "after this, therefore in consequence of this." *Post hoc* is the logical fallacy of assuming that a subsequent event is the result of a preceding one merely because of sequence. In *post hoc* thinking, because Event B occurs after Event A, B is thought to be *caused by* A. For example, suppose that you pick and eat a green apple. An hour later, you develop a severe stomachache. "Owww!" you complain, "that green apple has given me the worst stomachache of my entire life!" Perhaps it did; perhaps it didn't. Maybe the pizza or the banana split you also ate caused your suffering. Maybe it was the three of them together. Or maybe you are coming down with intestinal flu!

The excerpts below contain examples of *post hoc* fallacies. Read each excerpt carefully. Then, identify Events A and B, describe the fallacy, and offer two other possible causes for Event B.

Miranda: (*excitedly*) Oh, Muffin, you lucky dog! I have a brand new puppy food just for you. (*pours food into dog dish*) It's called Attapup.
Muffin: (*eagerly*) Arf! Arf!
Miranda: Yes, yes, I know that you are a very hungry puppy. (*pats Muffin on the head affectionately*)
Muffin: Yip! Yip! (*bites Miranda*)
Miranda: Ouch! Oh, you nasty puppy! You shouldn't bite me just because you don't like your new food.

Detective: Just let me get this straight, Ma'am. You gave your nephew twenty thousand dollars to invest?
Mrs. Grant: (*obviously exasperated*) Yes, yes! How many times do I have to repeat this story? I gave Anton the twenty thousand dollars.
Detective: And then?
Mrs. Grant: He took the money and said that he would invest it for me. (*angrily*) That was the last I heard from him!
Detective: How long ago was that, Ma'am?
Mrs. Grant: Precisely one week. He doesn't answer his phone. He's gone, absconded with my life savings. I've been robbed, ruined!

Event A: _____

_____

Event B: _____

_____

Post hoc fallacy: _____

_____

Two other possible causes of Event B:

(1) _____

_____

(2) _____

_____

Event A: _____

_____

Event B: _____

_____

Post hoc fallacy: _____

_____

Two other possible causes of Event B:

(1) _____

_____

(2) _____

_____

Two Plus Two Plus Two Equals Infinity

You may not realize it, but you are already familiar with the fallacy of **improper distribution.** This fallacy is the assumption that the whole is the sum of its parts—no more, no less—or that the parts *always* add up to the whole. For example, you might assume that, by sleeping one hour less each night, you could have an additional seven hours at the end of the week, but you would be wrong! Time is not distributed in this fashion. By sleeping one hour less each night, you *will* have one more waking hour each day, but you will not have a lump of seven hours at the end of the week.

Read the arguments below. On the lines under each argument, write **yes** or **no** to indicate whether it does or does not rest on the fallacy of improper distribution and explain your answer.

1. One excuse people often give for not exercising is lack of time. Here's a suggestion for you busy homemakers who have trouble fitting exercise into your schedules. Instead of doing the dishes three times a day, do them only once, in the evening. Those extra minutes you save throughout the week can add up to several hours of jogging time each weekend.

   _____

   _____

   _____

2. No, Coach Brootal, I cannot allow you to hold basketball practice from 3:00 until 4:30 each day after school; however, you can have the gym from noon until 7:30 on Saturdays. That will give you the seven and one-half hours of weekly practice you seem to feel the team needs.

   _____

   _____

   _____

3. **Ms. Newsprint:** And to what do you attribute your phenomenal success in business, Mr. Sterling?
   Mr. Sterling: Time management, Ms. Newsprint, time management. I don't waste unnecessary time eating. I eat breakfast while riding to work in a taxi, and I bring my lunch. In this way, I arrive an hour earlier each morning and take only a few minutes for lunch. This routine allows me to work nearly ten hours a day instead of the usual eight.

   _____

   _____

   _____

Name_____

Or You'll Be Sorry

Another barrier to logical thinking is the false or **misleading either-or statement**. In a statement of this kind, a situation is characterized as consisting of only two possibilities (either-or) or choices; whereas, in reality, it may consist of many more. For example, consider this statement: "Either this door is locked or it is stuck." Does this statement describe a true either-or situation? Might the door be *both* locked and stuck? If the door is locked, its being so does not preclude its also being stuck; and there might be other plausible explanations for its failure to open readily. For instance, somebody might be holding it closed, you might be too weak to open it, or it might be nailed shut.

Read each statement below. If the situation it describes is really an either-or, write **yes** on the line. If it is not, write **no** on the line and explain your answer.

1. Collin, you get in the house this minute or you'll be sorry.

_____

_____

2. Either this patient has the measles or she does not.

_____

_____

3. The person who hung up when I answered the phone was either making a crank call or was extremely embarrassed at having dialed the wrong number.

_____

_____

4. We are faced with a choice too frightening to contemplate: either we achieve peace in the Middle East immediately or we prepare to fight World War III in this long-troubled area.

_____

_____

5. Either there is a burglar in the house or the cat just knocked over something.

_____

_____

Unload That Question!

Loaded questions, serious barriers to logical communication, are often based on false either-or assumptions. These questions are phrased in such a way that the person to whom they are addressed must choose between two answers, neither one of which may be entirely correct and both of which may put him at a disadvantage or show him in a bad light. For instance, a teacher might ask, "Well, Al, have you finally quit cheating on exams?" If Al answers "yes," he seems to be admitting that he cheated in the past but has now stopped; but if he answers, "no," he is implying that he still cheats. In short, the question has been loaded against Al. It offers him two undesirable alternatives. No matter how he responds, Al simply can't win.

First, read the questions below. Second, circle the number of each one that is "loaded." Finally, rewrite each loaded question to give the person who must answer it a fairer chance and/or a wider choice.

1. Have you ever cheated on a test?

_____

2. Do you want to be Sharon's partner or mine?

_____

3. Are colds caused by the weather or by stress?

_____

4. Have you finally learned how to budget your money?

_____

5. Is your weight problem under control?

_____

6. Does anyone know what causes asthma?

_____

7. Do you want to pay the entire bill now or leave a down payment?

_____

8. Have you always had trouble controlling your temper?

_____

9. Is mental illness caused by stress or by pollution?

_____

10. Do you think that, in the future, you can get along better with your co-workers?

_____

Name _____

Finding the Connection

An **analogy** is a relationship or correspondence between one pair of terms that serves as the basis for the creation of another pair. The terms in the second pair have the same relationship to each other as do the terms in the first pair. Some possible relationships are:

1. One word is a **synonym** for the other.
   Example: Rip is to tear as raze is to demolish.
2. One word is an **antonym** of the other.
   Example: Mend is to tear as erect is to demolish.
3. One word is a characteristic **part** of the other.
   Example: Fiber is to cloth as brick is to wall.
4. One word is a **kind** of the other.
   Example: Silk is to cloth as tile is to roof.

Analogies are often used in communication. Usually, their purpose is to help the listener or reader understand an unfamiliar concept or relationship in terms of a familiar one. But sometimes their purpose is to confuse the issue and persuade the listener or reader to accept a point or premise that he might otherwise reject.

Read the analogies below. Identify the relationship between the terms in each pair by writing a letter on the line in front of each analogy. Write **s** if one word is a **synonym** for the other, **a** if one word is an **antonym** of the other, **p** if one word is a **part** of the other, and **k** if one word is a **kind** of the other.

_____ **1.** *Finger* is to *hand* as *toe* is to *foot.*

_____ **2.** *Hot* is to *cold* as *wet* is to *dry.*

_____ **3.** *Rose* is to *flower* as *oak* is to *tree.*

_____ **4.** *Careless* is to *irresponsible* as *cautious* is to *careful.*

_____ **5.** *Up* is to *down* as *high* is to *low.*

_____ **6.** A *galley* is to a *ship* as a *kitchen* is to a *house.*

_____ **7.** *Persian* is to *cat* as *poodle* is to *dog.*

_____ **8.** *Broad* is to *wide* as *slender* is to *thin.*

_____ **9.** *Petal* is to *flower* as *bristle* is to *brush.*

_____ **10.** *Truck* is to *vehicle* as *pineapple* is to *fruit.*

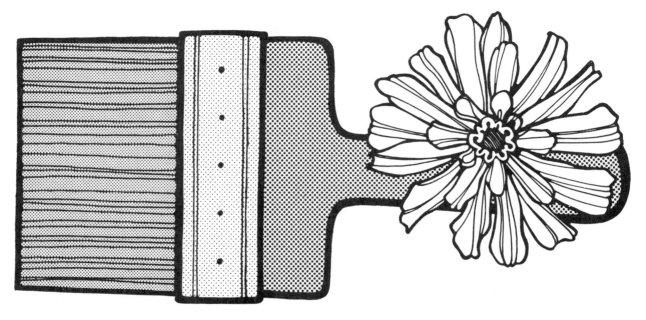

Name_____

A Is to *B* as *C* Is to *D*

An **analogy** is a relationship or correspondence between one pair of terms that serves as the basis for the creation of another pair. The terms in the second pair have the same relationship to each other as do the terms in the first pair.

To complete these analogies, choose two words from the list below each sentence and write them on the lines.

1. _____ is to *eye* as *sound* is to _____.
   (ear, hearing, lash, nose, sight)

2. *Big* is to _____ as *tall* is to _____.
   (giant, larger, little, short, thin)

3. *Faucet* is to _____ as _____ is to *electricity*.
   (fountain, light, switch, water, wiring)

4. *Now* is to _____ as _____ is to *there*.
   (always, here, never, then, this)

5. *Standing* is to _____ as *floating* is to _____.
   (boating, fishing, flying, swimming, walking)

6. _____ is to *4* as *4* is to _____.
   (even, odd, 2, 8, 16)

7. _____ is to *base* as *body* is to _____.
   (feet, ground, marble, skyscraper, statue)

8. *Love* is to _____ as *hot* is to _____.
   (chilly, cold, friend, hate, steam)

9. *Dog* is to *puppy* as _____ is to _____.
   (adult, brother, child, kitten, son)

10. _____ is to _____ as *hat* is to *head*.
    (bonnet, comb, foot, hair, shoe)

11. *Steering wheel* is to _____ as *reins* are to _____.
    (car, horse, horseman, ride, tire)

12. *Good* is to *better* as _____ is to _____.
    (best, warm, warmer, warmest, well)

13. *Fly* is to *frog* as _____ is to _____.
    (beetle, cat, dog, mouse, pond)

14. *Top* is to _____ as _____ is to *foot*.
    (above, bottom, finger, hand, head)

15. *Road map* is to _____ as _____ is to *computer programming*.
    (car, computer, flowchart, keyboard, traveling)

Name_____

Analogously Speaking

In literature and in everyday communication, analogies are often used to help the reader or listener understand an abstract concept or an unfamiliar process. When analogies are used in this way, something that is abstract or unfamiliar is explained in terms of something that is concrete or familiar. Thus, the analogy becomes a way of explaining one thing in terms of another.

Analogies used in this way are seldom in strict *A*-is-to-*B*-as-*C*-is-to-*D* form. Therefore, you must look more closely at analogies of this kind to discover what the speaker or writer is explaining, what comparison he or she is using, and how valid it is.

Read these analogies. On the line below each one, explain what things are being compared.

1. Shakespeare wrote:

> How like a winter hath my absence been
> From thee, the pleasure of the fleeting year!
> —Sonnet 97, lines 1–2

_____

_____

2. William Congreve wrote:

> Women are like tricks by sleight of hand,
> Which, to admire, we should not understand.
> —*Love for Love* (1695)
> Act II, scene 2

_____

_____

3. Henry Wadsworth Longfellow wrote:

> A feeling of sadness and longing
> That is not akin to pain,
> And resembles sorrow only
> As the mist resembles rain.
> —"The Day Is Done" (1845)

_____

_____

4. Abraham Lincoln said:

> "A house divided against itself cannot stand." I believe this government cannot endure permanently half slave and half free.
> —Speech, Republican State Convention
> Springfield, Illinois (June 16, 1858)

_____

_____

Name _____

How Did You Come to That Conclusion?

An **inference** is an educated guess based on facts or premises. In the inference process, reasoning based on what is known is used to come to a conclusion about what is unknown. Because something is unknown, inferences are sometimes incorrect.

You frequently make inferences. For example, if you see a friend crying, you infer that something or someone has upset him. You are probably correct, but you could be wrong. Your friend might be rehearsing for a play or might have gotten an irritating substance in his eyes.

One commonly made inference is the assumption that **negation** of a term is the same thing as its **opposite.** For instance, if Jim says, "I *don't like* Tom," you might infer that Jim *dislikes* Tom. If you do so, you have confused *not like* (the negation of *like*) with *dislike* (the opposite of *like*). Your inference may be incorrect because Jim may not know Tom well enough either to like or to dislike him. In other words, Jim may not yet have formed any opinion about Tom or may have neutral feelings about him, feelings that can be classified neither as *like* nor as *dislike*.

Read the four brief dialogues below. For each one, identify the inference and explain the possible flaw in this reasoning.

1. **Richard:** Janine doesn't think that song is *good*.
   Laura: I knew she would think it was *bad*.

   Inference: _____

   _____

   Possible flaw: _____

   _____

2. **Hotel Guest:** Sir, the doorman's greeting to me was *not* friendly!
   Hotel Manager: That's impossible! Our doorman does *not* greet guests with hostility.

   Inference: _____

   _____

   Possible flaw: _____

   _____

3. **Teacher:** The twins are not quick learners.
   Parent: Are you saying that *my* children are slow learners?

   Inference: _____

   _____

   Possible flaw: _____

   _____

Name_____

Historical Inferences

Below are some facts from history. First, explain what was inferred based on these facts. Then, label each inference **C** if it was **correct** or **I** if it was **incorrect.**

_____ **1.** When you look across water or a vast expanse of land, you see a relatively flat, horizontal line where the earth and sky meet. From this fact, people who lived long ago inferred that ____

_____.

_____ **2.** Nightshade is a poisonous plant. Tomatoes are members of the nightshade family. When the tomato, a plant native to Mexico and Peru, was first introduced into Europe during the sixteenth century by Spanish explorers, it was called the love apple and was grown solely for ornamental purposes because Europeans inferred that _____

_____.

_____ **3.** Settlers who came to America from Europe in the 1800s were accustomed to two kinds of land, heavily forested areas and deserts. After they had pushed westward across the Mississippi River, they encountered a vast expanse of treeless land. They inferred that this land was _____

_____.

_____ **4.** In the 1800s, Ignaz Semmelweis, a Hungarian obstetrician, noted that most of the women who died from puerperal fever after childbirth had something in common. They had been attended by doctors who had previously handled sick patients or cadavers without washing their hands afterward. From this information Semmelweis inferred that _____

_____.

_____ **5.** Simon Fraser, a Canadian explorer, was commissioned by the North West Company of Canada to explore the Columbia River to its mouth. Hoping to reach the Columbia through its upper waters, Fraser and his men journeyed along a stream they thought to be the upper Columbia. When, at last, the waterway they were following emptied into a broad bay, they inferred that _____

_____.

Name_____

Infer Away

Study this scene very carefully. Then make five different inferences about what has happened. Write your inferences on the lines below.

1. _____

_____

2. _____

_____

3. _____

_____

4. _____

_____

5. _____

_____

From General to Specific

A **deduction** is an inference in which the conclusion reached follows necessarily from the premises. In logic, **premises** are statements that are assumed to be true and are used to draw a conclusion.

In **deductive reasoning**, the specific is derived from the general, or the individual, from the universal. One example of this form of reasoning is scientific classification, a process in which large categories are first defined or described and individual examples are then matched to them. For instance, consider the following example of deductive reasoning:

General definition: Insects are invertebrate animals with three distinct body parts and only three pairs of legs.
Specific description: The grasshopper is an invertebrate animal with three distinct body parts and only three pairs of legs.
Conclusion: The grasshopper is an insect.

The statements labeled *general definition* and *specific description* are actually premises. In the example above, the general definition is the **major premise**, and the specific description is the **minor premise**. Notice that a conclusion reached by deductive reasoning cannot contain more information than was contained in the original premises and may contain less.

On the lines below, provide two examples of deduction, or deductive reasoning.

1. a. **General definition:** _____

   _____

   b. **Specific description:** _____

   _____

   c. **Conclusion:** _____

   _____

2. a. **General definition:** _____

   _____

   b. **Specific description:** _____

   _____

   c. **Conclusion:** _____

   _____

Name_____

Baseball, Football, or Golf?

Deductive reasoning is a process used to derive the specific from the general. Here is a typical problem in deductive reasoning.

> Together, Tom, Dick, and Harriette play baseball, football, and golf. No two of them play the same sport. Dick does not play golf. Tom plays baseball. Harriette does not play football. Which sport does each of these students play?

To solve this problem, (1) make a grid (called a **matrix**), (2) follow the instructions below, and (3) write your answers on the lines provided in instruction 10.

People	Sports		

1. Write the names of the students (**Tom, Dick,** and **Harriette**) in the three boxes down the left-hand side of the matrix.

2. Write the names of the sports (**baseball, football,** and **golf**) in the three boxes across the top of the matrix.

3. Because the problem states that Dick does not play golf, write an **x** in the box where the **Dick** row meets the **golf** column.

4. Because the problem states that Tom plays baseball, write the word **yes** in the box where the **Tom** row meets the **baseball** column.

5. Because you know that Tom plays only one sport (baseball), write an **x** in the box where the **Tom** row meets the **football** column.

6. Again, because you know that Tom plays only one sport (baseball), write an **x** in the box where the **Tom** row meets the **golf** column.

7. Because the problem says that no two of these three people play the same sport and that Tom plays baseball, you know that Dick and Harriette do *not* play baseball. Write an **x** in the box where the **Dick** row meets the **baseball** column.

8. Write an **x** in the box where the **Harriette** row meets the **baseball** column.

9. Because the problem states that Harriette does *not* play football, write an **x** in the box where the **Harriette** row meets the **football** column.

10. Look at the matrix. By following these nine steps, you have deduced that _____

_____ plays baseball, _____ plays football, and _____ plays golf.

Name_____

Likes and Dislikes

   To solve the deductive reasoning problem below, you must deal with three people and two sets of facts. Read the problem and set up your matrix. Write the names of the three people in the boxes down the left-hand side of the matrix. Write the names of the three foods and of the three colors in the boxes across the top of the matrix. Then write the letter **x** or the word **yes** in the boxes where the people rows intersect the food and color columns. Remember to use **yes** to indicate that a person likes a food or color and to use an **x** to indicate that a person does *not* like a food or color. Finally, record your answers on the numbered lines at the bottom of this page.

   Abby, Brenda, and Charles each like certain foods and certain colors; but they cannot agree on any of their preferences. Everything that Abby likes, Brenda and Charles dislike. Everything that Brenda likes, Abby and Charles dislike. Everything that Charles likes, Abby and Brenda dislike. Abby loves beef. Brenda thinks red is too bold; she doesn't like this color at all. Charles loves chicken. Abby thinks that, because she has blonde hair, she looks best in black, a color she absolutely adores. Abby and Charles think that pizza is too messy to eat; they dislike it. Brenda loves pizza. Charles loves the color that Brenda thinks is too bold. Brenda likes green and wears it frequently because she thinks that it enhances the color of her eyes.

People	Foods			Colors		

1. Abby likes _____and _____.

2. Brenda likes _____and _____.

3. Charles likes _____and _____.

Name_____

Take Me Out to the Ball Game

Use what you have learned about deductive reasoning (see pages 36–38) and the matrix drawn below to solve this problem. Record your conclusions in the answer table at the bottom of this page.

Ella, John, and Sam are avid baseball fans. Although all of them readily agree that baseball is their favorite sport, none of them can agree on favorite teams or players. They each have a different favorite team and an all-time favorite batter and pitcher. One of the favorite batters is Babe Ruth, who played for the New York Yankees. One favorite pitcher is the legendary Satchel Paige. Another favorite pitcher is Bob Gibson. Ella's favorite team is the Yankees. Another favorite team is the St. Louis Cardinals. Henry Aaron is someone's favorite batter, but not John's. Ella's favorite batter did not play for her favorite team. John's favorite pitcher is Lefty Gomez. John does not like the Boston Red Sox, but one of the other two fans claims this team as his favorite. One person's favorite pitcher's first name starts with the same letter as his own name. Ella's favorite batter is Willie Mays.

Matrix

	Teams			Batters			Pitchers		
People									

Answer Table

People	Teams	Batters	Pitchers

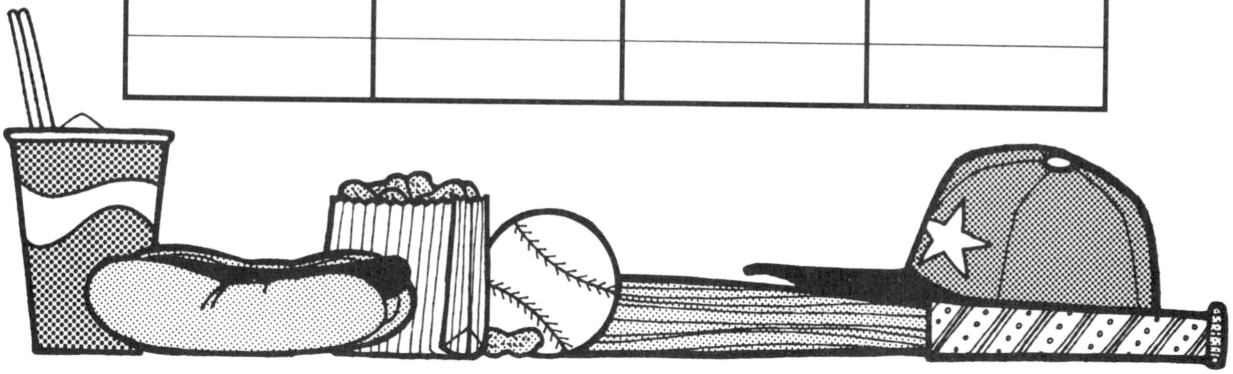

Syllogistically Speaking

A **syllogism** is a pattern for deductive reasoning. All syllogisms consist of three statements and three terms. **The statements** are called the **major premise**, the **minor premise**, and the **conclusion.** For example, consider the following syllogism:

Major premise: All bears are brown.
Minor premise: Bruno is a bear.
Conclusion: Bruno is brown.

The **three terms** are distributed throughout the three statements so that each term appears twice within the syllogism. For purposes of identification and analysis, these terms are usually labeled with the letters **A, B,** and **C.** Look at this syllogism again and notice how the terms are distributed.

	A	**B**
Major premise:	All *bears* are	*brown.*

	C	**A**
Minor premise:	*Bruno* is a	*bear.*

	C	**B**
Conclusion:	*Bruno* is	*brown.*

If you are uncertain about whether a particular statement sequence or reasoning pattern is or is not a syllogism, count the number of statements and the number of terms. If you find fewer or more than three of either one, the sequence or pattern is *not* a syllogism.

With this definition in mind, decide whether the numbered statement sequences below are or are not syllogisms. Read each one carefully. If it is a **syllogism**, write the letter **S** on the line to the left of the number. If the sequence is **not a syllogism**, write the letter **N** on the line to the left of the number and explain your answer.

Syllogisms are often used to assess the truth of premises or to prove a conclusion. For this exercise, however, do not consider whether a syllogism is valid or invalid or whether its premises are true or false.

____ **1.** All cats are cunning.
Tuffy is a cat.
Tuffy is cunning.

_____

_____

____ **2.** No dogs are friendly.
Fang is my dog.
Fang is a Doberman.

_____

_____

____ **3.** Some flowers smell nice.
The hibiscus is a flower.
The hibiscus smells nice.

_____

_____

____ **4.** Some flowers smell terrible.
The carrion flower smells terrible.
The carrion flower grows in Africa.
Other flowers grow in Africa.

_____

_____

____ **5.** All human beings are mammals.
The elephant is an animal.
The elephant is a mammal.

_____

_____

____ **6.** All human beings are mammals.
Tom is a human being.
Tom is a mammal.

_____

_____

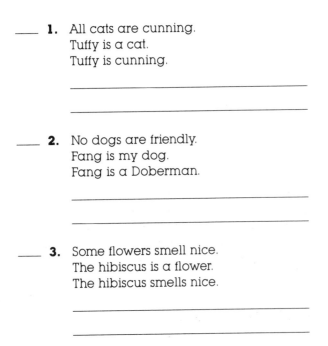

Name_____

All of the Above

A syllogism is either valid or invalid. A **valid syllogism** conforms to the laws of logic, that is, its conclusion is correctly derived from its premises. An **invalid syllogism** is logically inconsequent or inconclusive.

You can test the validity of a syllogism by diagramming it. Below are diagrams of two "all" type syllogisms. Study these diagrams carefully.

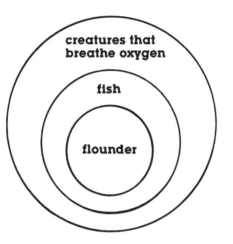

Syllogism 1
All fish breathe oxygen.
The flounder is a fish.
The flounder breathes oxygen.

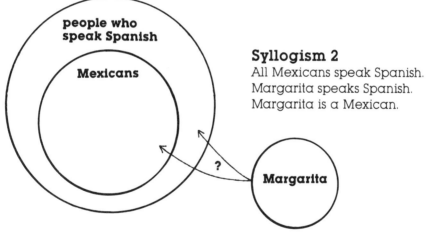

Syllogism 2
All Mexicans speak Spanish.
Margarita speaks Spanish.
Margarita is a Mexican.

The first syllogism is valid because the flounder falls within the circle of fish, and the circle of fish falls within the larger circle of creatures that breathe oxygen. The second syllogism is invalid because, while we know Margarita belongs inside the larger circle of people who speak Spanish, we do not know from the information given whether she also belongs inside the smaller circle of Spanish-speaking people who are Mexican. The conclusion that Margarita is Mexican cannot be logically derived from the premises because we have been told that *all Mexicans speak Spanish,* not that *only Mexicans speak Spanish.* For this reason, the second syllogism is invalid.

Name_____

None of the Above

In the activities on page 41, you were introduced to "all" type syllogisms. Below are two "no" type syllogisms. Read these syllogisms and study their diagrams carefully.

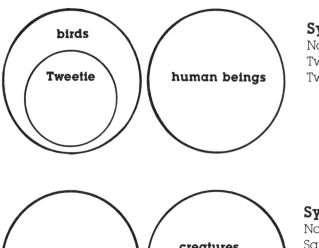

Syllogism 1
No birds are human beings.
Tweetie is a bird.
Tweetie is not a human being.

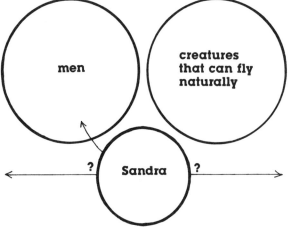

Syllogism 2
No man can fly naturally.
Sandra cannot fly naturally.
Sandra is a man.

As you can see, the first syllogism is valid. Because of the word *no*, the circles of birds and human beings are mutually exclusive. In other words, the major premise states that a creature cannot be both a bird and a human being. The minor premise states that Tweetie is a bird; therefore, because of the mutual exclusivity established by the word *no*, Tweetie cannot also be a human being.

The second syllogism is invalid. Although the circles of men and creatures that can fly naturally are mutually exclusive and we are told in the minor premise that Sandra does not belong in the circle of creatures that can fly naturally, there is no information in either premise from which we can conclude that Sandra belongs in the men circle. She might, in fact, belong to another group of creatures that also cannot fly naturally. Remember, while we have been told that no man can fly naturally, we have not been told that men are the *only* creatures that cannot fly naturally.

Name_____

Some of the Above

In the activities on pages 41 and 42, you were introduced to "all" and "no" type syllogisms. The third type of syllogism is the "some" type syllogism. Below are two "some" syllogisms. Read these syllogisms and study their diagrams carefully.

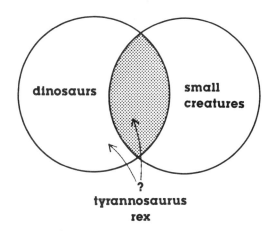

Syllogism 1
Some dinosaurs were small.
Tyrannosaurus rex was a dinosaur.
Tyrannosaurus rex was small.

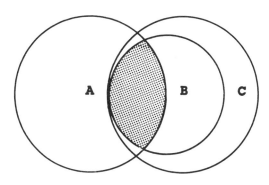

Syllogism 2
Some **A** are **B**.
All **B** are **C**.
Some **A** are **C**.

The first syllogism is invalid. Although the dinosaur and small creature circles overlap and tyrannosaurus rex was a dinosaur, we have no way of knowing from the information given in the premises whether tyrannosaurus rex was a small dinosaur, a medium dinosaur, or a large dinosaur. In fact, tyrannosaurus rex was a large dinosaur and ranks as the largest meat-eating land animal that has ever lived; but the syllogism does not tell us so. Remember that, in assessing the validity of a syllogism, we can use only the facts presented in the premises and not other information of which we may be aware.

The second syllogism is valid. The major premise states that some **A** are **B**. Thus, the **A** circle and the **B** circle overlap. This overlapping is indicated by shading. The minor premise states that all **B** are **C**. For this reason, the **C** circle must be drawn so that it contains all of the **B** circle, including the shaded portion where **A** and **B** overlap. Thus, some of the **A** circle falls within the **C** circle, confirming that some **A** are **C**.

Name_____

True or False, Valid or Invalid

The validity of a syllogism is not necessarily related in any way to whether the premises are true or false. Below are some syllogisms. For each one, place an **x** in the appropriate box to indicate whether the major premise is true or false and whether the syllogism is valid or invalid.

	Premise		Syllogism	
	True	False	Valid	Invalid

1. Some students are intelligent.
Some students are adults.
Some adults are intelligent.

2. Some anarchists are untrustworthy.
Kelly is untrustworthy.
Kelly is an anarchist.

3. No cars are safe.
Zip is a car.
Zip is not safe.

4. All books are enjoyable.
All toys are enjoyable.
All toys are books.

5. No insects have eight legs.
A spider has eight legs.
A spider is not an insect.

6. All bears are brown.
Bruno is a bear.
Bruno is brown.

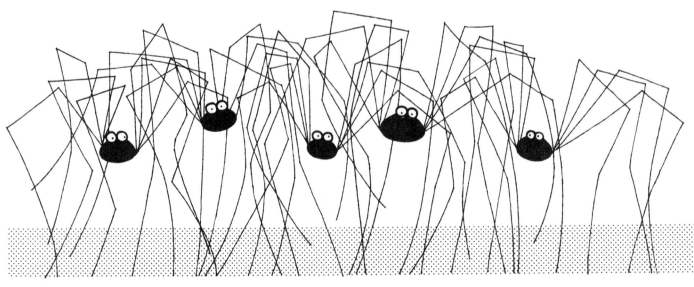

Answer Key

Page 6, Is That a Fact?
Statement numbers 1, 3, 6, 7 and 9 should be circled because these statements are facts.

Page 7, Seeking Verification
Statements 1, 4, and 5 can be verified.
Statements 2 and 3 cannot be verified.
Comments: 2. Louisiana's northern border is the thirty-third parallel, not the thirty-second parallel. 3. The words attributed to Nathan Hale were actually spoken by Patrick Henry.

Page 8, Now It Is, Now It Isn't
Answers will vary, but each one should express an attitude, evaluation, or judgment.

Page 9, Opinions! Opinions!
1. O, P
2. G, J
3. P
4. P
5. J
6. J
7. G
8. O
9. J
10. J
11. G, J
12. J
13. P
14. O
15. J

Page 10, Get the Facts, Please
Answers may vary slightly, depending on the source. According to information given on page 65 of the 1982 edition of the *Information, Please, Almanac*, reading from top to bottom in the order needed, the figures are as follows:

346,367	1,082,274
164,351	934,633
2,565,776	4,949,395
2,037,185	5,083,957
1,467,553	2,979,284
902,902	3,679,126

Page 11, Watch Those Numbers!
Sentences may vary but should be based on the actual numbers represented by the potentially misleading percentages used to support the opinions.

Page 12, Says Who?
1. V
2. I
3. P
4. V
5. V
6. I
7. V
8. I
9. P
10. V
11. P
12. P
13. V
14. V
15. V

Page 13, Might and Right
Summaries and explanations will vary.

Page 14, Meaning What?
1. i
2. b
3. a
4. n
5. l
6. g
7. j
8. m
9. h
10. c
11. e
12. d
13. f
14. o
15. k

Page 15, How Do You Respond?
Because connotations vary from person to person, responses will vary.

Page 16, What Do You Say?
Circled word choices and connotations may vary. The connotations listed below are intended to serve only as examples.
1. *sweat:* extremely hard work requiring tremendous physical effort
perspire: mild exertion
2. *girl:* immaturity and lack of respect
woman: sufficient maturity to accept the responsibility of employment
3. *bug:* a disgusting live but unidentified creature
insect: more scientific or analytical approach with emphasis on the intellectual (identification) rather than on the emotional (disgust)
4. *male:* cold and impersonal
man: warmer, more personal, and more specific
5. *teenager's:* wild and irresponsible youth; specific demographic and/or cultural group
young person's: greater respect; less definite age identification; no association with a specific demographic and/or cultural group

Page 17, In a Pickle
1. *United States:* The United States of America did not exist before the Revolutionary War and so could not have sent representatives to the British Parliament, even if permitted or invited to do so. A better term would be *American colonies* or *American colonists.*
2. *steel:* Steel is not a natural resource. Instead, it is a substance produced by refining a natural resource, iron, to improve its malleability and lower its carbon content.
3. *pickles:* Mark did not grow pickles in his garden. Instead, he grew fruits or vegetables, such as cucumbers, peaches, or watermelon, and produced pickles by preserving them in brine or vinegar.
4. *lunar day:* While there are twenty-four hours in each solar day, there are twenty-four hours and fifty minutes in each lunar day.

Page 17, In a Pickle (continued)

5. *tics:* Tics are jerky facial movements often caused by nervousness or a nervous disorder; and if a dog had them, a flea collar would not help. Ticks, on the other hand, are bloodsucking arachnids that attach themselves to warm-blooded vertebrates, including dogs, to feed. It is possible that the insecticide on a flea collar would be effective against ticks.

6. *murdered:* Murder means "to kill a person unlawfully and with premeditated malice." Because Susan's act was an accident and did not involve premeditation, she may be guilty of vehicular manslaughter or of homicide, but she is not guilty of murder.

Page 18, Round and Round

1. The way to look up definitions and/or spellings in a dictionary.

2. Rewritten versions will vary but might include the following information: Be careful! Remember that the word *pneumonia* begins with the silent letter *p.* It is spelled p-n-e-u-m-o-n-i-a. Now apply what we have learned about alphabetical order.

Pages 19, How Does That Fit?

1. f 2. c, g, n 3. a, g 4. h, o 5. e, k

Page 20, Speak to Me, Please!

1. b 2. a 3. a 4. a 5. b
Relevant sentences will vary.

Page 21, Does It Follow?

1. a. The customer wants to exchange a warped record.
   b. Their first album was much better.
   c. If you have your sales receipt, I'll be glad to make the exchange.
2. a. Shouldn't women receive equal pay for equal work?
   b. Women miss a lot of workdays.
   c. Yes, they should, when they do the same work and assume the same responsibilities as men. You seem to be unaware, however, that Mr. Braden has been with this company far longer than you have and that our union-endorsed salary scale is designed to reward lengthy and continuous service.
3. a. Do you smoke, Doctor?
   b. I think I'm qualified to take care of my own health, don't you?
   c. *Either* yes *or* no.

Page 21, Does It Follow? (continued)

4. a. Glamorous Hollywood stars use Lovelier-You Lotion.
   b. If stars use it, you should try it.
   c. Not necessarily.

Page 22, Address the Issue
Rewritten dialogues will vary but should be both logical and relevant and should not be characterized by *argumentum ad hominem,* that is, attacks on character rather than on facts or argument.

Page 23, So's Your Old Man!
Original dialogues will vary and should include neither *argumentum ad hominem* nor *tu quoque* or be rife with both, depending on which option the student chooses.

Page 24, Double, Double, Toil and Trouble
Both general principles and double standards will vary.

Page 25, All That Glitters—Is Not Clear or True!
Questions will vary but should be logically constructed and designed to strip away the glitter.

Page 26, And Then He Absconded
First Excerpt
Event A: Miranda gave Muffin a new dog food and patted him.
Event B: Muffin bit Miranda.
Fallacious assumption: Muffin bit Miranda because he didn't like the food.
Other possible explanations:
(1) Muffin does not like to be patted or otherwise interfered with while he is eating.
(2) Miranda stepped on Muffin's paw.
Second Excerpt
Event A: Mrs. Grant gave Anton twenty thousand dollars.
Event B: Mrs. Grant could not reach Anton by telephone.
Fallacious assumption: Anton took the money and left town.
Other possible explanations:
(1) Anton's telephone was out of order.
(2) Anton's telephone had been disconnected.
(3) Anton was ill and unable to come to the phone.
(4) Anton left town unexpectedly but had invested the money as promised.

Answer Key
(continued)

Page 27, Two Plus Two Plus Two Equals Infinity

1. Yes. You cannot save minutes each day and have them add up to hours at the end of a week. Also, several hours of jogging once a week probably will not constitute a safe and effective exercise program.

2. Yes. Seven and one-half hours of practice once a week will not have the same cumulative effect as one and one-half hours of practice five times a week.

3. No. Mr. Sterling actually does gain time to work each day. Of course, he may develop indigestion or ulcers, but his method produces the results he attributes to it.

Page 28, Or You'll Be Sorry

1. No. The tone of this statement suggests that Collin is likely to be sorry, or regret his actions, no matter what he chooses to do.

2. Yes.

3. No. The caller might have hung up abruptly because an emergency or other situation demanded immediate attention.

4. No. The choice is not between immediate peace and immediate war. And if the explosive Middle East situation is defused, war may break out elsewhere.

5. No. The apparently unexplained noise might have been made or caused by a member of the household, another pet, or the wind.

Page 29, Unload That Question!

Numbers 2, 3, 4, 5, 7, 8, 9, and 10 should be circled. Rewritten versions may vary. The following responses are examples of what is expected:

2. Whose partner would you like to be?
3. What are some of the recognized causes of the common cold?
4. How do you budget your money nowadays?
5. Have you found a safe and effective way to control your weight?
7. How do you want to pay for your purchase?
8. Do you have trouble controlling your temper?
9. Are stress and pollution causes of mental illness?
   What are some of the recognized causes of mental illness?
10. Do you think you will be able to get along with your co-workers?

Page 30, Finding the Connection

1. p	5. a	8. s
2. a	6. p	9. p
3. k	7. k	10. k
4. s		

Page 31, A Is to B as C Is to D

1. sight, ear
2. little, short
3. water, switch
4. then, here
5. walking, swimming
6. 2, 8
7. statue, feet
8. hate, cold
9. adult, child
10. shoe, foot
11. car, horse
12. warm, warmer
13. mouse, cat
14. bottom, head
15. traveling, flowchart

Page 32, Analogously Speaking

1. The unpleasantness of winter and absence from a loved one; also, the loved one's presence and pleasure.

2. Women and magic, which are both more fascinating when they cannot be completely explained or wholly understood.

3. A particular sadness is to sorrow as mist is to rain.

4. A house (*or* family) in which there is dissension and a government (*or* nation) in which there is disagreement on a fundamental issue.

Page 33, How Did You Come to That Conclusion?

1. *Inference:* If Janine does not think that the song is good, she must think that it is bad.
   Possible flaw: Janine may be undecided or may think that the song is better than bad but not really good.

2. *Inference:* If a greeting is not friendly, it must be unfriendly or even hostile.
   Possible flaw: The doorman's "not friendly" greeting could have been cool, indifferent, or reserved without being unfriendly or hostile.

3. *Inference:* If the twins are not quick learners, they must be slow learners.
   Possible flaw: The twins may actually be neither quick nor slow but average. By definition, many people are.

Answer Key
(continued)

Page 34, Historical Inferences
1. I – the earth was flat
2. I – it was poisonous
3. I – a desert
4. C – the doctors were transmitting the disease
5. I – they had traced the course of the Columbia River from its source to its mouth

Page 35, Infer Away
Inferences will vary.

Page 36, From General to Specific
Examples of deductive reasoning will vary.

Page 37, Baseball, Football, or Golf?

People	Sports		
	baseball	football	golf
Tom	yes	x	x
Dick	x	yes	x
Harriette	x	x	yes

10. Tom plays baseball, Dick plays football, and Harriette plays golf.

Page 38, Likes and Dislikes

People	Foods			Colors		
	beef	chicken	pizza	red	black	green
Abby	yes	x	x	x	yes	x
Brenda	x	x	yes	x	x	yes
Charles	x	yes	x	yes	x	x

1. Abby likes beef and black.
2. Brenda likes pizza and green.
3. Charles likes chicken and red.

Page 39, Take Me Out to the Ball Game
Answer Table

People	Teams	Batters	Pitchers
Ella	Yankees	Willie Mays	Bob Gibson
John	Cardinals	Babe Ruth	Lefty Gomez
Sam	Red Sox	Henry Aaron	Satchel Paige

Page 40, Syllogistically Speaking
1. S
2. N This statement sequence contains four terms.
3. S
4. N This statement sequence consists of more than three statements.
5. N This three-statement sequence contains four terms (i.e., human beings, mammals, elephant, and animal).
6. S

Page 44, True or False, Valid or Invalid
1. true, invalid
2. true, invalid
3. false, valid
4. false, invalid
5. true, valid
6. false, valid

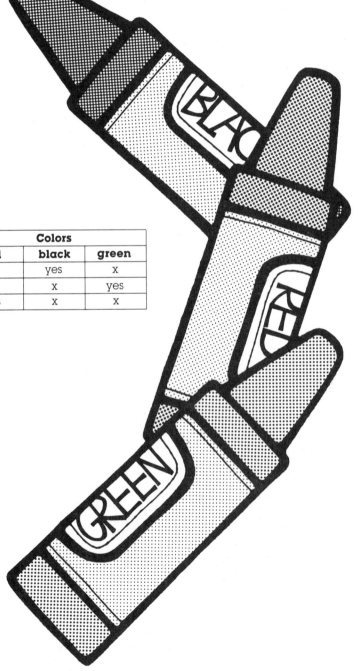